Christmas Doodles

Buster Books

Illustrated by Piers Harper

First published in Great Britain in 2008 by Buster Books,
an imprint of Michael O'Mara Books Limited,
9 Lion Yard, Tremadoc Road,
London SW4 7NQ

A CIP catalogue record for this book is available
from the British Library.

ISBN: 978-1-906082-30-7

10 9 8 7 6 5 4 3 2 1

Printed and bound in China by Imago

What is on top of the tree?

It's time to build some snowmen.

Heap the bowl with sweets.

What is in the toy shop window?

Who is coming for Christmas?

Put on a pantomime.

Give us party hats.

Decorate your Advent calendar.

What is inside the doors?

Draw Santa a bushy beard.

Decorate the biscuits.

Baubles or puddings?

Fill the sky with snow.

What are the elves making?

Hide presents in the house.

Cover the gifts in pretty paper.

Fill the sky with stars . . .

...and add chimneys for Santa.

What is for Christmas breakfast?

Design a Christmas e-greeting.

Who is Mum kissing under the mistletoe?

Yikes – what a Christmas jumper!

Decorate the stockings.

What is in the snow globe?

Who threw that snowball?

Build the world's best snowman.

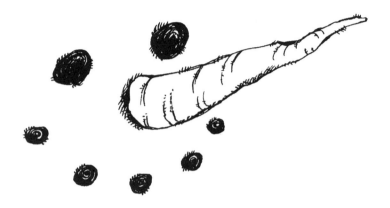

Decorate the baubles.

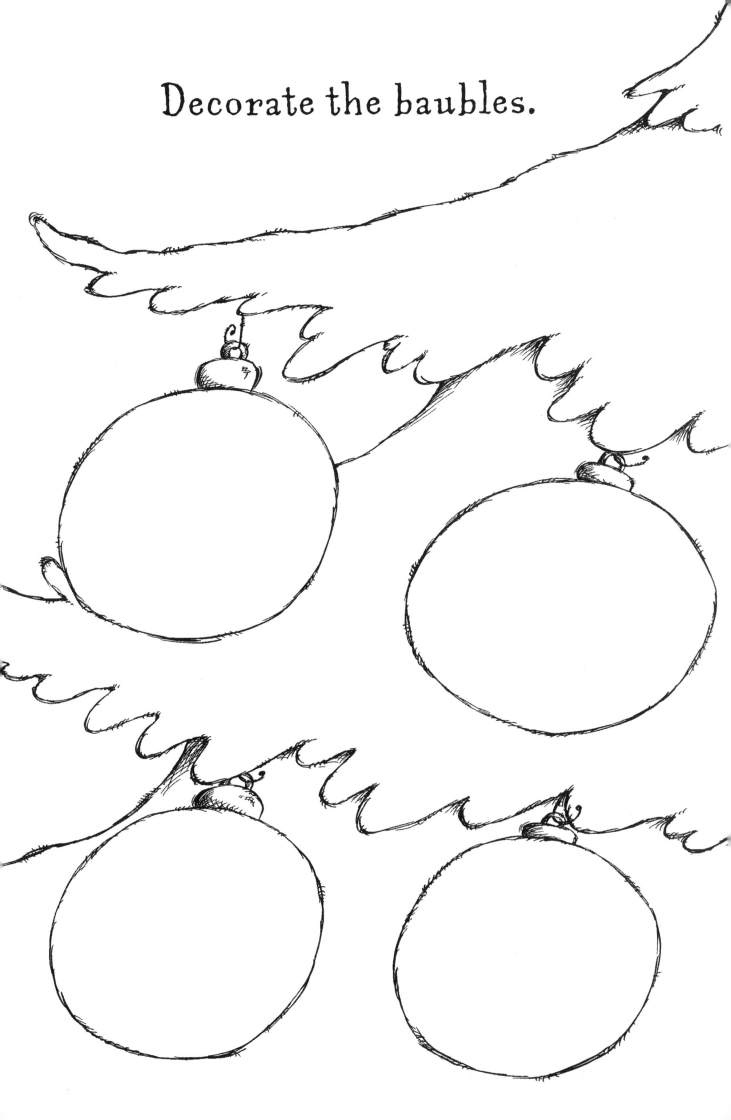

Do they like their presents?

What was left out for Santa?

Can you complete Santa?

Who slipped on the ice?

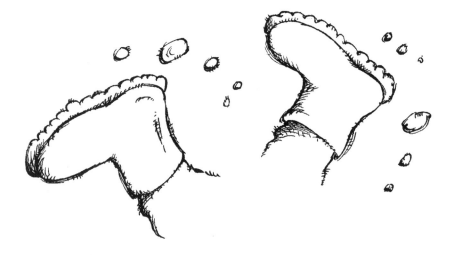

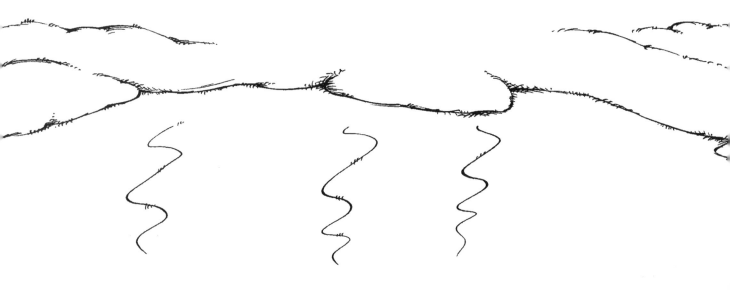

Design your own seasonal stamps.

What movie did you watch?

Give the reindeer some antlers.

Decorate the windows.

Jump out of bed on
Christmas morning!

Decorate the tree.

What treats are in the cupboard?

Decorate the Christmas cake.

Design your own Christmas card.

Fill the plate with mince pies.

Stack up the snowballs.

Pile up the parcels.

Draw the tallest tree in the forest.

Finish the festive pattern.

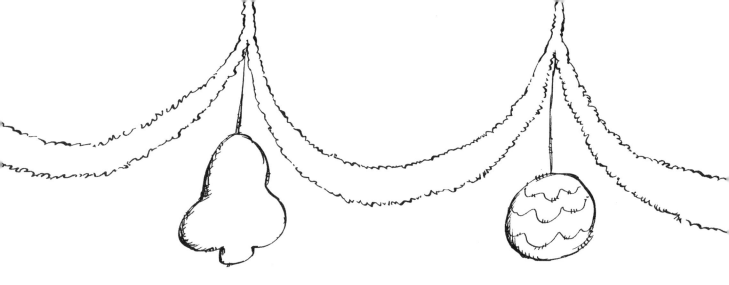

Fancy dress!

Whose footprints?

What presents did the pets get?

Ding-dong bells.

What games are they playing?

Decorate the bedroom.

Make the fireplace festive.

Cover the house with fairy lights.

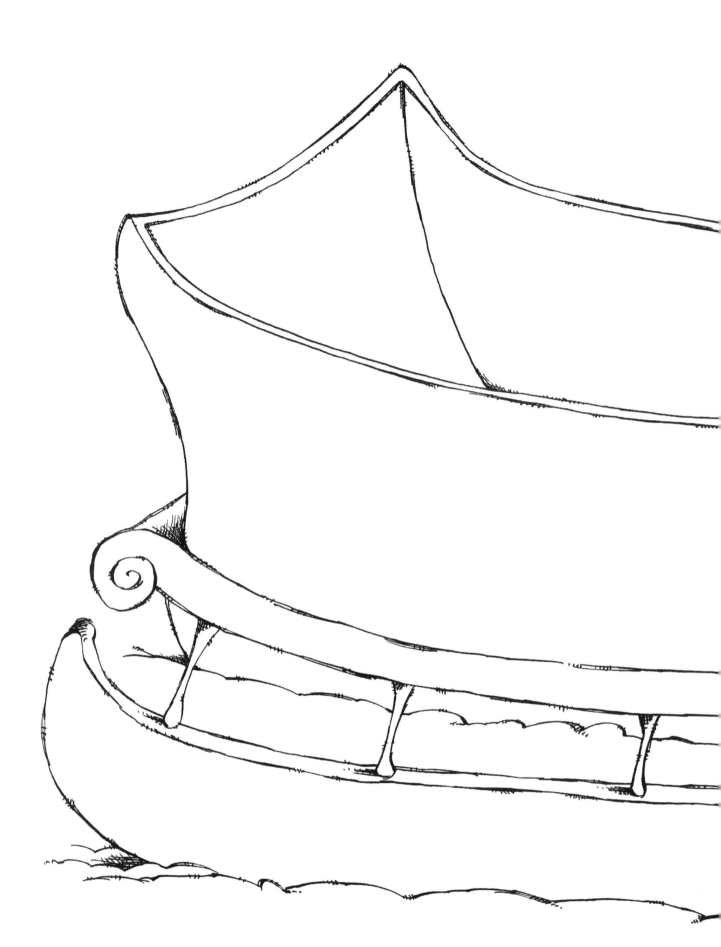

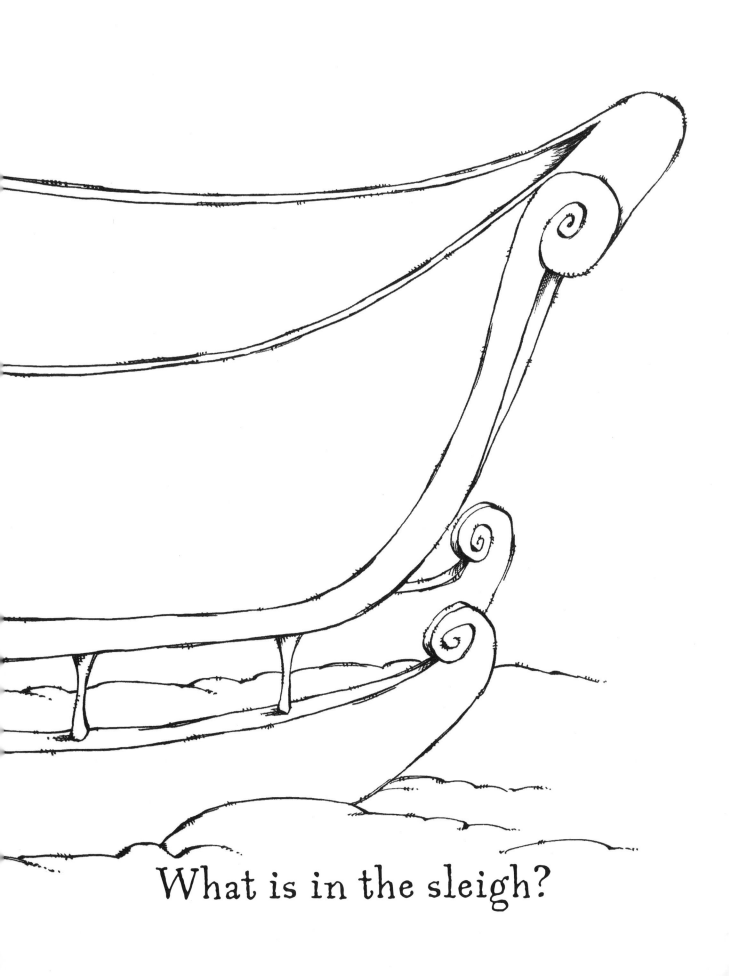

What is in the sleigh?

Finish the wreath on the door.

Give them great skating outfits.

Write a Christmas poem.

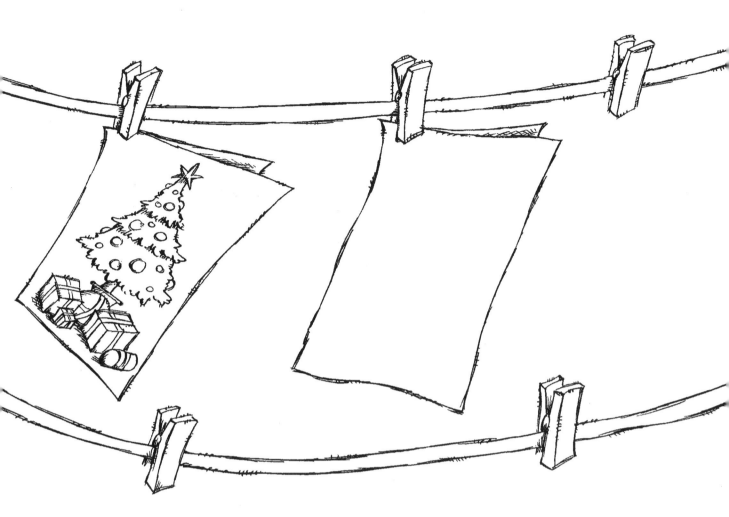

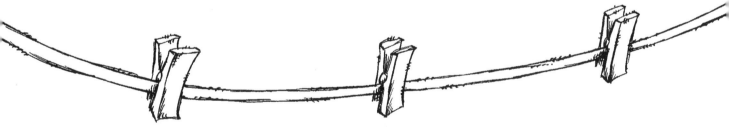

Draw the cards on the line.

Look at Dad's Christmas socks!

Pile the presents under the tree.

Draw your favourite Christmas gifts.

Can you finish Rudolph?

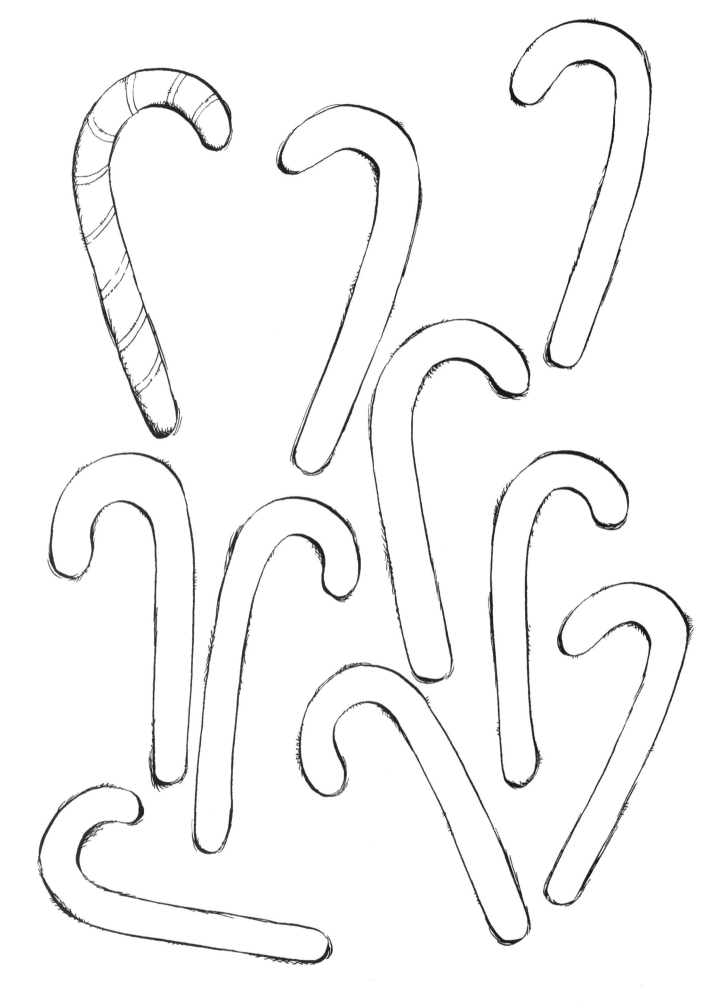

Colour in the candy canes.

What an amazing ice sculpture!

Add more Christmas lanterns.

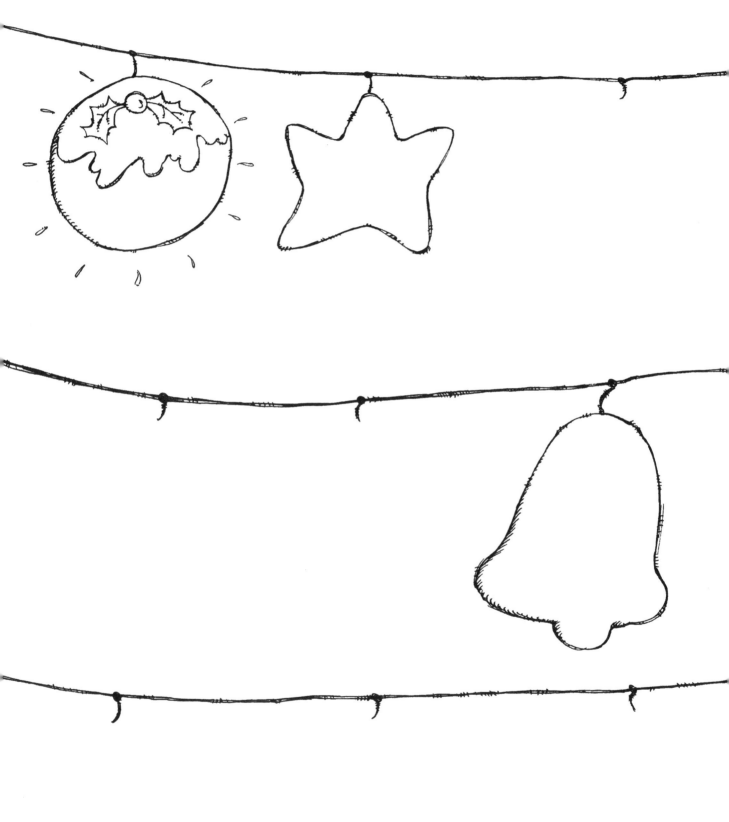

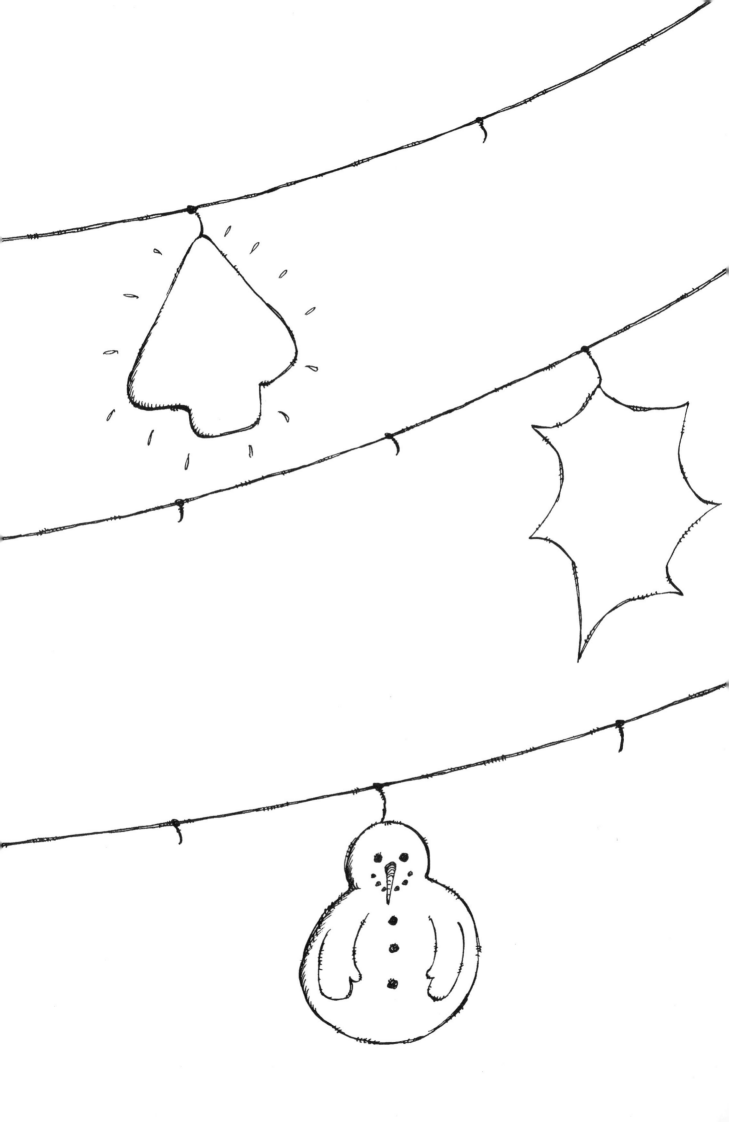

Draw Dad some wicked wellies.

Help Santa get to the fireplace.

Put berries on the holly.

Fill the sky with robins.

Snowflakes glisten ...

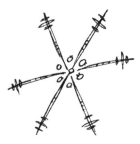

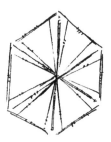

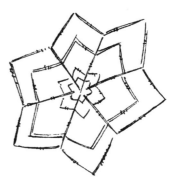

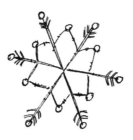

Put icicles around the window.

Build more snow animals.

Biscuits or birds?

Snowball fight!

Give Dad the longest scarf ever.

Pop on some woolly hats.

What was outside on Christmas Eve?

Fill the hamper with festive goodies.

What did Santa drop?

What is for Christmas dinner?

Who is singing carols?

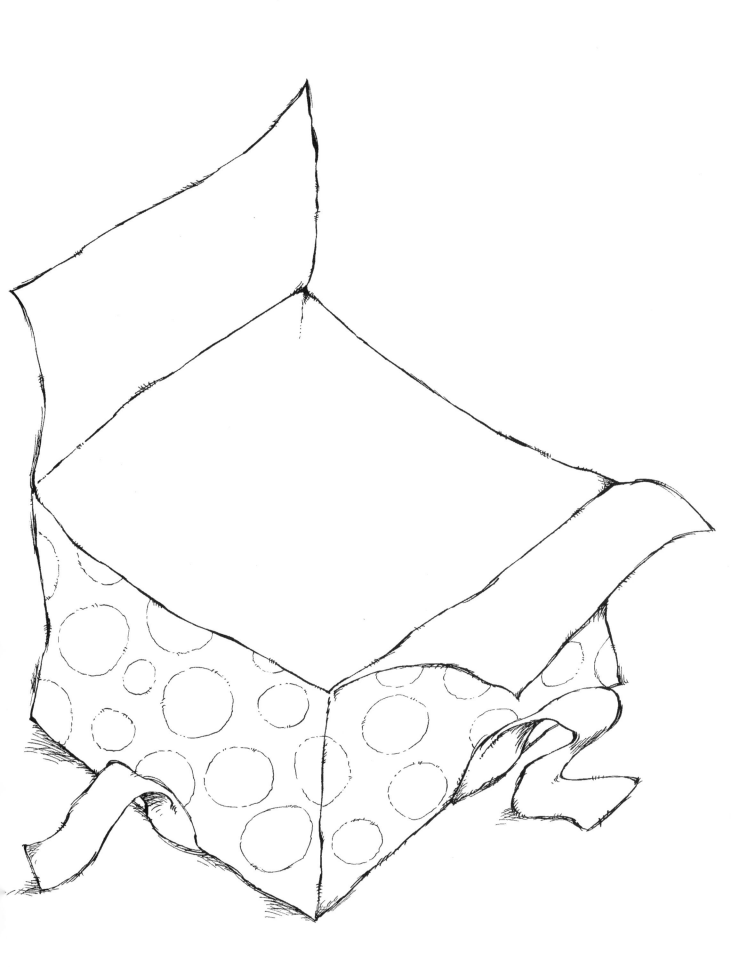

What is in the gift box?

What is for pudding?

Who fell asleep after lunch?

Who ate the mince pie?

What's in the sack?

Who made the snow angels?

Draw the Christmas parade.

Who is sledging?

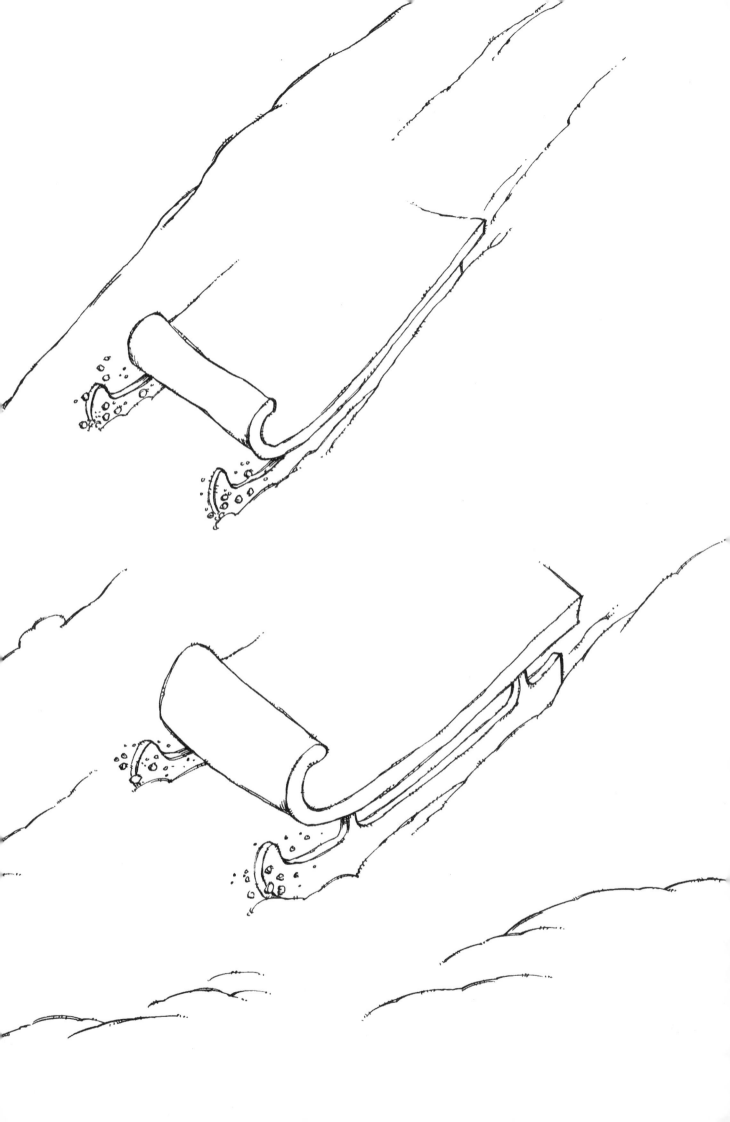

Put party hats on the puppies.

What is on next year's Christmas list?

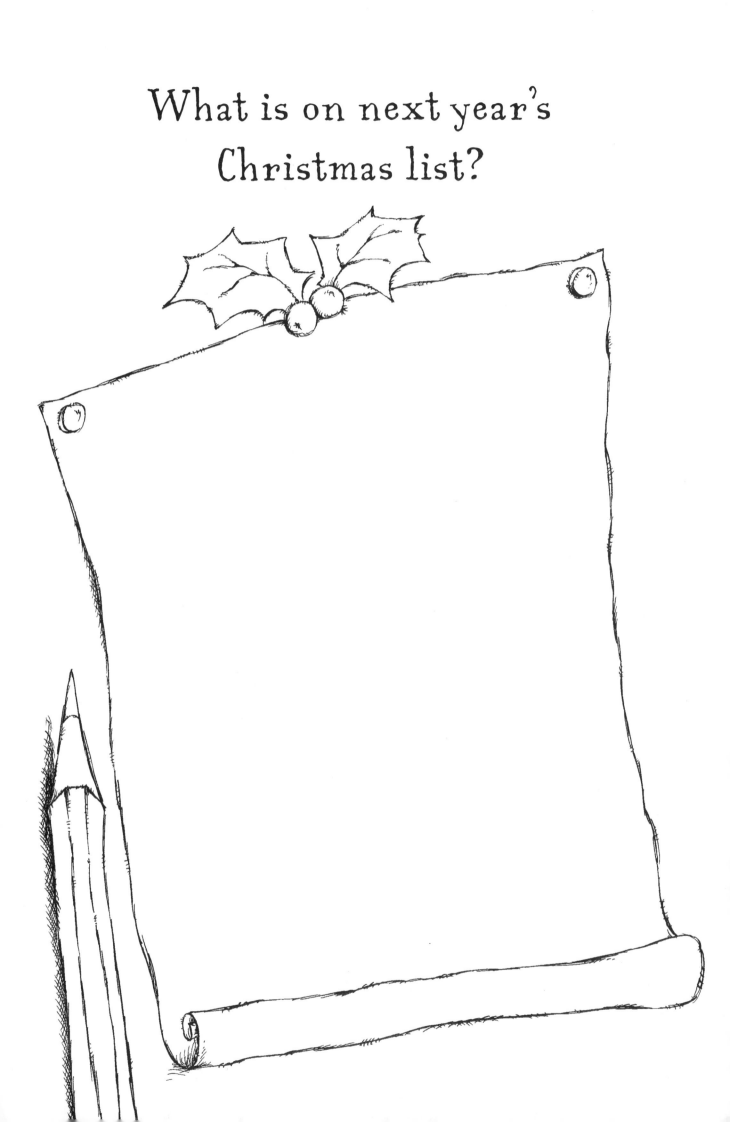

The best present in the world.

The worst present in the world.

What is missing?

Which Christmas gifts will go in the jumble sale?

Make your New Year's resolutions.